Usborne English

Level 2

GULLIVER'S TRAVELS

Retold by Laura Cowan

Illustrated by George Ermos

English language consultant: Peter Viney

Contents

You can listen to the story online here:
usborneenglishreaders.com/
gulliverstravels

Gulliver was a ship's doctor. He used to sail all around the world. After many years of travels, he wanted to stay at home with his family, but he agreed to one last job. His ship was sailing to the South Seas, far away from his home in England.

One night there was a terrible storm.
The ship hit a rock and broke into pieces.
Gulliver swam away as the ship went under
the water. Finally he reached an island. He
was so tired that he lay down on the shore
and went to sleep.

The next morning, Gulliver woke up.
He tried to stand, but he couldn't move his
head, his arms or his legs at all. Something
was holding him down on the ground, and he
could only see the sky.

He heard a noise, and felt something on
his leg, but he couldn't move to look at it.
The thing walked up his body until it reached
his head. Then Gulliver saw a tiny man. The
man was holding a bow and arrow.

Many more tiny men ran up his body, so Gulliver shouted at them. They were terrified, and most of them ran away or fell off.

A few men reached his face. They started shouting at him in funny little voices, but he couldn't understand their language.

Gulliver was a strong man, and he pulled his hand up. He saw tiny ropes around his fingers, and he could feel lots more ropes all over his body.

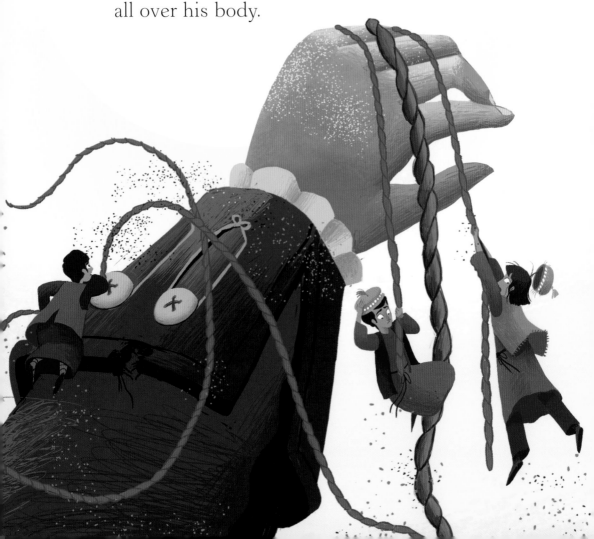

The ropes were tying him to the ground. The tiny people shouted some more, and shot their tiny arrows at him. Gulliver was quiet after that, and he didn't move again.

After a while, one of the tiny people started speaking to him. Gulliver didn't understand the words, but he listened carefully. He learned the name of this new land: Lilliput.

Then the men brought him tiny cooked chickens and sheep to eat. They ran up his body and dropped them into his mouth. The meat was delicious, and Gulliver was very hungry. He ate happily.

The next day, many more tiny people
visited Gulliver. First came a man
and a woman with all their children. They
were wearing beautiful red, gold and purple
clothes and valuable jewels. Hundreds of
tiny servants followed them.

"They must be important," thought
Gulliver, and he was right. They were the
Emperor of Lilliput, the Empress and the
little princes and princesses.

The Emperor shouted at Gulliver a lot. Gulliver answered in several different languages, but the Emperor didn't understand any of them.

Then the Emperor had an idea. His men began building a big wooden machine on wheels.

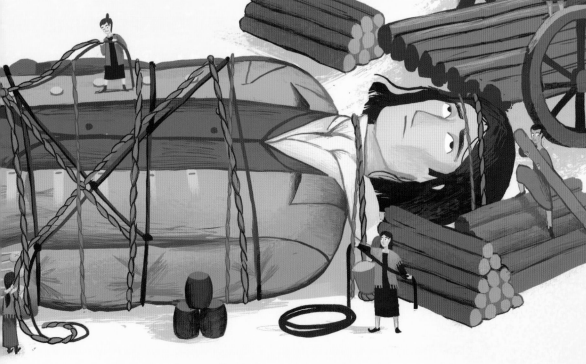

Hundreds of them carried Gulliver onto it and pushed it all the way to their city. The machine moved very slowly, and the journey took days.

When they arrived, the men put Gulliver in an empty temple. This was the biggest building in the city. They untied his ropes and put a chain around his foot instead.

Gulliver slept on the cold stone floor, and it was very uncomfortable. The Lilliputians could see that, so they built him a bed. They used six hundred of their own beds, and sewed six hundred of their blankets together.

Gulliver needed a lot of food.
He ate as much food every day as
hundreds of Lilliputians. Hundreds of
them had to cook his meals and bring
them to him. Hundreds of others
sewed new clothes for him.

In the next few weeks, Gulliver learned many things about this strange new country. The cleverest men in Lilliput came to the temple and taught him their language.

When Gulliver could understand Lilliputian, a man came to visit him. His name was Skyresh, and he was the most important person in the Emperor's government.

Skyresh brought a paper for Gulliver, with a long list of all the things that Gulliver must and mustn't do. He could walk on big roads, but not on small ones. He mustn't walk over Lilliputians or their homes. He had to carry letters for the Emperor, and fight against the Lilliputians' enemies.

When Gulliver finally agreed to everything on the list, the Emperor's men took away his chain.

Gulliver walked to the Emperor's palace. He cut down some trees in the royal garden and made a chair for himself. He wanted to know more about the Lilliputians, so he sat outside the Emperor's palace and watched them through the windows.

The Lilliputians opened all the windows so that he could see the people inside.

One Lilliputian became Gulliver's friend. His name was Reldresal, and he often visited Gulliver in the temple. One day, he was very worried. "Lilliput is in danger!" he said. "It's a long story, but let me explain.

When the Emperor's grandfather was Emperor, everyone ate eggs from the big end. That was normal for us. Then one morning, the Emperor was cutting the big end of his egg when he hurt his finger on his knife."

"After that, everyone had to eat their eggs from the small end. There was a terrible war, and thousands of people died because they didn't agree."

"Now the Big-endians can't work in Lilliput's government, and no one can even read books about them. Many Big-endians left Lilliput and went to live on the island of Blefuscu."

"Lilliput and Blefuscu are enemies now. Lilliput lost forty ships and thirty thousand men in the last war. We've just heard that ships from Blefuscu are sailing across the sea to Lilliput! Gulliver, can you help us?"

"Of course I'll help you. You're my friends," Gulliver told him.

He walked into the sea. When the
Blefuscans saw Gulliver, they were
terrified. They jumped into the sea
and swam all the way back to their
island. Gulliver picked up the
ropes of the empty ships,
and pulled fifty of them
back to Lilliput.

The Emperor was very pleased. "You are now a Nardac," he told Gulliver. "That means you're one of the most important men in Lilliput. You're almost as important as me."

Skyresh was jealous of Gulliver. This stranger – this Man Mountain – was a Nardac, but Skyresh wasn't. He couldn't say anything, though. Nobody could disagree with the Emperor.

"Now, Nardac Man Mountain, you must help me to fight Blefuscu. We will make all Big-endians our slaves," the Emperor said.

"I'm sorry, Emperor, but I won't do that," said Gulliver. "I can't make free people into slaves."

The Emperor was angry too, now. He didn't say anything, but he couldn't stop thinking about it. He decided he didn't like Gulliver so much.

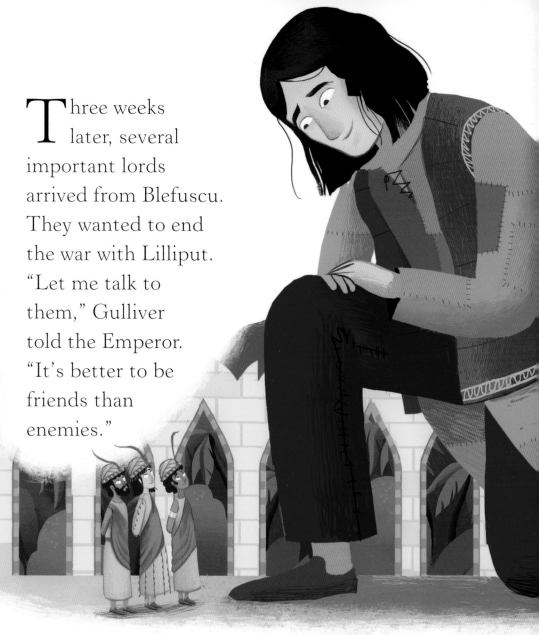

hree weeks
later, several
important lords
arrived from Blefuscu.
They wanted to end
the war with Lilliput.
"Let me talk to
them," Gulliver
told the Emperor.
"It's better to be
friends than
enemies."

"The Man Mountain wants to help
Blefuscu more than Lilliput," Skyresh said
to the Emperor, and the Emperor agreed.
Gulliver didn't know this, though. He was
already talking to the Blefuscans.

Some days later, Gulliver woke up in the
night. People were shouting "Fire!" Gulliver
jumped out of his bed and went outside.
The royal palace was on fire, and the
Empress's rooms were burning.

Gulliver wanted to help. He couldn't find
any water, but then he had an idea. He sat
down on the palace roof. The fire burned
his coat, but his big bottom put out the fire
easily and he saved the palace.

The Empress was very angry. "The Man Mountain's bottom has destroyed my rooms!" she said. "I can never use them again." She often talked to Skyresh, and soon they were both making plans against Gulliver.

Skyresh spoke to the Emperor. "Sir, this Man Mountain costs too much," he said. "Hundreds of your people work all day to cook his food and make his clothes. Nobody has time to do anything else. He's too expensive." The Empress agreed.

"Maybe you're right," said the Emperor. Nobody was happy with Gulliver now.

One night, Reldresal visited Gulliver's temple secretly. "I have some bad news," he said. "Skyresh and the Empress say you are an enemy of Lilliput." He showed Gulliver a list of his crimes. The crimes were sitting on the palace roof, and making friends with the people of Blefuscu.

"But I saved the palace! And I only spoke to the Blefuscan lords because I wanted to end the war," Gulliver said.

"I know, but the Emperor was angry because you didn't fight them. Skyresh wants to hurt you or even kill you. He wants to burn this temple and then shoot you with arrows," Redresal told him sadly. "You have so many enemies, Gulliver. Everyone listens to Skyresh and the Empress."

"*They* want to hurt *me*?" shouted Gulliver. "I can easily destroy the palace, and all the houses in the city!"

"No, Man Mountain, you must leave Lilliput. You should go to Blefuscu instead."

Early the next morning, Gulliver took the
blanket from his bed and went to the shore.
He took off his clothes, put them in his
blanket and put everything in a ship. Then
he walked across the sea to Blefuscu, pulling
the ship on a rope behind him.

At first the Blefuscans were frightened, but
Gulliver told them his story. Then they were
happy to see him. "Any enemy of Lilliput is a
friend of Blefuscu," they said.

They were kind to Gulliver, but Gulliver
didn't have a home there, or even a bed.
He had to sleep on the ground outside. He
wrapped his blanket around himself, but he
was still cold and uncomfortable.

A few days after he arrived in Blefuscu, Gulliver was walking by the sea. Suddenly he saw something in the water. It was a boat, from a ship like his old one!

The Blefuscans helped Gulliver to bring the boat to the shore, then they helped him to fix it and get ready for a long journey.

While this was happening, the Emperor of Lilliput sent a message to Blefuscu. "Gulliver must come back immediately," he said. "If he doesn't come back in two hours, you must tie him with ropes and send him here."

The Emperor of Blefuscu laughed. "I can't do that. He's much too strong! Anyway, the Man Mountain is planning to sail home, so your Emperor won't have to worry about him."

Then he told Gulliver. "You can stay here with us if you want. We are your friends."

Gulliver thanked him, but he still wanted to go home. A month later, his boat was ready. The Emperor gave him some tiny cows and sheep to eat on his journey, and some more to take back to England. He also gave Gulliver a picture of himself, and lots of Blefuscan money. Gulliver wrapped the picture in some cloth and put it in his pocket.

Two days after Gulliver left Blefuscu, an English ship found his boat in the South Seas. Gulliver's story was very strange, but he showed everyone the tiny sheep and cows, the bags of money and the little picture of the Emperor. Then they had to believe him.

When the ship reached England, people paid lots of money to see the tiny animals. Gulliver was rich, and he was happy to be home for a while.

Soon, though, he wanted to travel again. "What strange new places are out there?" he wondered, "and what strange new people? If there are tiny people, maybe there are much bigger ones, too."

About the story

Jonathan Swift came from an English family, but he lived for most of his life in Dublin, Ireland. He wrote *Gulliver's Travels* in 1726. It was originally called *Travels into Several Remote Nations of the World by Lemuel Gulliver.* It is Swift's most famous book, and there are lots of films of the story.

The Lilliput story is only one part of *Gulliver's Travels*. In other parts, Gulliver visits a land of giants, a flying island and a land of talking horses. In this picture you can see Gulliver with some of the people of Brobdingnag, the country he visits after Lilliput. Although Gulliver is afraid of the giants at first, they are friendly and kind to him – friendlier than the tiny Lilliputians.

Activities

The answers are on page 40.

A strange new country

Choose the right word to finish each sentence.

1.

Gulliver ...... a tiny man.

heard hurt saw

2.

The men ...... him tiny cooked chickens and sheep to eat.

brought lent threw

3.
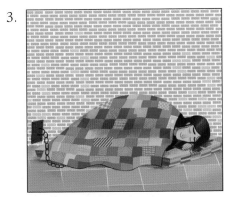

The men ...... Gulliver in an empty temple.

found hid put

4.

The cleverest men ...... him their language.

gave taught told

Mixed-up story

Can you put these pictures and sentences in order?

A.

"The Man Mountain's bottom has destroyed my rooms!"

B.

Gulliver pulled the ropes of the empty ships back to Lilliput.

C.

Reldresal showed Gulliver a list of his crimes.

D.

"You are now a Nardac," said the Emperor.

E.

Gulliver was happy to be home for a while.

F.

A month later, Gulliver's boat was ready.

G.

"I can't make free people into slaves," said Gulliver.

H.

He walked across the sea to Blefuscu.

I.

Gulliver wanted to help.

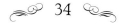

Who says this?

Match the words to the right person.

Skyresh

The Empress

Reldresal

The Emperor of Blefuscu

A.
You can stay here with us if you want. We are your friends.

B.
This Man Mountain costs too much.

C.
You have so many enemies, Gulliver.

D.
The Man Mountain's bottom has destroyed my rooms!

A long story

Choose the right sentence for each picture.

1.

  A. Everyone ate eggs from the big end.

  B. Everyone ate eggs from the best end.

2.

  A. The Emperor hurt his finger on his egg.

  B. The Emperor hurt his finger on his knife.

3.

  A. There was a terrible war and thousands of people died.

  B. There was a terrible war and thousands of people ran away.

4.

  A. Liliput and Blefuscu are strangers now.

  B. Lilliput and Blefuscu are enemies now.

How does Gulliver travel...
Choose the right answer to each question.

Carried on a cart   Sailing on a ship   Swimming

Sailing on a small boat   Walking through the sea

1.

...to the South Seas?

2.

...to the island of Lilliput?

3.

...to the Lilliputians' city?

4.
...to the island of Blefuscu?

5.

...away from Blefuscu at the end of the story?

Word list

arrow (n) a thin piece of wood with a sharp point. Long ago, people used bows and arrows for fighting or to chase and kill animals (hunting).

blanket (n) a big cloth, often used as a warm cover on a bed.

bottom (n) the part of your body that you sit on.

bow (n) a long piece of wood with a tight string. It is used to shoot arrows for fighting and hunting.

chain (n) something like a rope, made of heavy circles of metal. It is sometimes used to stop a person or an animal from running away.

crime (n) when you do something illegal, it is a crime. For example, stealing is a crime.

destroy (v) when you destroy something, it is very badly broken and you can never use it again.

emperor (n) someone who is even more important and powerful than a king.

enemy (n) someone who is the opposite of a friend and wants to hurt you.

government (n) an important group of people who make decisions about how a country works and what it can do. Sometimes they do this for a king or queen or another important person.

journey (n) when you travel, you go on a journey.

list (n) words or phrases that you write one after the other, on lines. Sometimes you might number the lines. This page has new words from the story in a list.

lord (n) a rich and important man.

rope (n) something you use to tie things together, or to tie around things so that you can pull them.

sail (v) when a boat travels from one place to another, it sails.

save (v) to stop someone being killed or hurt, or something being destroyed.

sew (v) to fix two pieces of cloth together with a needle and thread. You can sew cloth together to make clothes.

shoot, shot (v) when you use a bow and arrow or a gun to hit something, you shoot.

shore (n) the land beside a river, lake or sea.

slave (n) someone who has to work for another person, but that person doesn't pay them.

temple (n) a religious building, where people pray to a god or gods.

terrified (adj) badly frightened.

tie, tying (v) you tie something with a string or rope so that it stays together, or so that it can't move.

tiny (adj) really small.

wrap (v) to cover someone or something with something else, for example a piece of cloth or paper.

Answers

A strange new country

1. saw
2. brought
3. put
4. taught

Mixed-up story

B, D, G, I, A,
C, H, F, E

Who says this?

Skyresh – B
The Empress – D
Reldresal – C
The Emperor of
Blefuscu – A

A long story

1. A
2. B
3. A
4. B

How did Gulliver travel..

1. Sailing on a ship
2. Swimming
3. Carried on a cart
4. Walking through the sea
5. Sailing on a small boat

 You can find information about other Usborne English Readers here:
usborneenglishreaders.com

Designed by Melissa Gandhi
Series designer: Laura Nelson Norris
Edited by Mairi Mackinnon
Digital imaging: Nick Wakeford

Page 32: portrait of Jonathan Swift © Culture Club/Getty Images
Scene from Gulliver's Travels by Jonathan Swift, 1911
© Photo by Ann Ronan Pictures/Print Collector/Getty Image

First published in 2020 by Usborne Publishing Ltd.,
Usborne House, 83-85 Saffron Hill, London EC1N 8RT, England.
usborne.com Copyright © 2020 Usborne Publishing Ltd.